TABLE OF CONTENTS

OPTIONS FOR ASSESSMENT IN

Informal Assessment and Self-Assessment	Portfolio Assessment	Managing Assessment	Performance Assessment

Informal Assessment and Self-Assessment

- **Informal Assessment boxes** throughout the *Teacher's Book* signal opportunities to assess students' work during instruction.

- The **Informal Assessment Checklist** helps in recording ongoing observations in group or individual formats.

- **Self-Assessment opportunities** appear in the *Teacher's Book* throughout each theme.

- **Integrated Theme Tests** and the **Benchmark Progress Tests** include additional self-assessment opportunities.

Portfolio Assessment

- **Portfolio Opportunities** in each theme are signaled by Portfolio icons.

- Opportunities include responding, comprehension, writing skills, word skills, communication activities, reading-writing workshop, and performance assessment activities.

- The Portfolio icon appears on *Literacy Activity Book* pages that are especially appropriate for portfolios.

- **Portfolio Assessment notes** in the *Teacher's Book* provide information on these topics: Introducing Portfolios to the Class, Selecting Material for the Portfolio, Grading Work in Portfolios, Conferencing with Students, Self-Assessment, Evaluating *Literacy Activity Book* Pages, Sending Work Home, Evaluating Oral Language, Peer Conferences, and Using Retellings to Evaluate Comprehension.

- The **Teacher's Assessment Handbook** includes practical teacher tips for organizing, maintaining, and using portfolios.

Managing Assessment

- **Managing Assessment notes** in the *Teacher's Book* provide practical tips for organizing and managing assessment.

- Topics include Theme Checklists, Testing Options, Work Samples, Report Cards, Making Expectations Clear, Parent Conferences, Monitoring Independent Work, Evaluating Writing, Keeping Anecdotal Notes, Planning Instruction, Setting Personal Goals, and Benchmark Progress Tests.

- Additional topics are included in the *Teacher's Assessment Handbook*.

Performance Assessment

- **Performance Assessment activities** with scoring rubrics appear at the end of each theme in the *Teacher's Book*. Topics include Making Story Strips, Making a Magazine Ad, Writing a Letter to the Captain, Planning a Picnic, Being Ready for a Storm, Making an Appointment Book.

- **Integrated Theme Tests** provide more extended performance options.

Instructional Planning and Placement

Baseline Group Tests

• **The Baseline Group Tests** can be given at the beginning of the year to evaluate students' instructional level and to plan the amount of support each student will need.

• The **Informal Reading Inventory** can be administered to individual students to gather additional information about their instructional level and individual instructional needs.

Integrated Theme Tests

Integrated Theme Tests

• **Apply theme skills** to a new authentic reading selection.

• Provide more extended performance assessment options.

• Can be given at the end of instruction for each theme.

• Have a format that reflects instruction.

• Integrate reading strategies, comprehension, word skills, writing, and language.

• Include written and multiple-choice answers.

• Can be adapted to meet individual needs.

• Have an easy-to-use Teacher's Edition with rubrics and sample answers at point of use.

• Have been proven in classroom field tests with over 4,900 students.

Theme Skills Tests

Theme Skills Tests

• **Test specific skills** taught in the theme.

• Include comprehension, word skills, writing, spelling, grammar, and study skills.

• Can be administered before the theme (pretest) or following the theme.

• Individual skill subtests can be administered separately.

• Have a multiple-choice format.

• Are in blackline-master format.

Benchmark Progress Tests

Benchmark Progress Tests

• **Assess students' reading level** and writing level compared to a national sample.

• Measure students' growth in reading and writing over time.

• Can be given at the beginning, middle, and end of the year.

• Have authentic reading selections including narrative and expository text.

• Are independent of program themes—can be scheduled independently.

• Use both written-answer and multiple-choice (multiple correct answer) formats.

• Have an easy-to-use Teacher's Edition with rubrics and sample student answers at point of use.

• Have been field tested with over 6,000 students.

• Have results correlated to standardized tests.

AUTHOR'S INTRODUCTION

Dear Educator:

Teachers have always used a variety of assessment strategies to help them evaluate student progress and to make instructional decisions. Taken together, these strategies can form a coherent assessment system.

A good assessment system includes three essential elements. First, it includes different types of informal and formal assessments. Second, it helps teachers integrate assessment during instruction and manage the use of classroom portfolios. Finally, both teacher and student self-assessment occur throughout the learning process.

Invitations to Literacy provides teachers with assessment options to fill all these needs. In this booklet you will find the Teacher's Edition of the Integrated Theme Tests and the corresponding Alternative Format Tests for each theme in Level 3.1.

Invitations to Literacy also provides extensive support for assessment integrated into the instructional plan in the *Teacher's Book*. There you will find theme Planning for Assessment, opportunities for Informal Assessment and student Self-Assessment, reminders for Portfolio Opportunities, Performance Assessment activities in the Theme Assessment Wrap-Up, and an Informal Assessment Checklist for each theme.

Not all teachers, students, or school districts need the same assessment system. By reviewing the various options in *Invitations to Literacy,* you can determine which pieces best meet your needs. Enjoy the many opportunities assessment provides to get to know your students and to help them grow.

Sheila Valencia

FEATURES AT A GLANCE

Integrated Theme Tests

✔ Apply theme skills to new authentic reading material.

✔ Include both narrative and expository text.

✔ Provide theme-related reading and writing tasks.

✔ Test in a format that reflects instruction.

✔ Integrate reading strategies, comprehension, word skills, writing, and language.

✔ Include written and multiple-choice answers.

✔ Can be used as performance assessment.

✔ Are easy to administer.

✔ Can be adapted to meet individual needs.

✔ Have an easy-to-use Teacher's Edition with rubrics and sample answers at point of use.

✔ Have been proven in classroom field tests with over 4,900 students.

USING THE INTEGRATED THEME TESTS

~ PURPOSE AND DESCRIPTION ~

Purpose

The Integrated Theme Tests evaluate students' progress as readers and writers in a format that reflects instruction. By providing an opportunity to apply skills to theme-related text selections, each Integrated Theme Test provides a holistic indicator of how well students have learned and are able to apply the skills and strategies developed in the theme.

Description

The Integrated Theme Tests include authentic reading selections and writing prompts that relate to the corresponding themes in the Anthology. Each test provides a main selection and a short related piece. One is narrative and one is expository. Students are asked to respond to the selections in four parts: Reading Strategies, Comprehension, Word Skills, and Writing and Language.

- **Reading Strategies:** While the best time to incorporate reading strategies is during classroom instruction, strategies are included in the test as a model of good reading practice and to help teachers evaluate how well students use them. The reading strategy questions are carefully placed within each selection depending on the text and the strategy.

- **Comprehension:** The Comprehension part is divided into two sections—written and multiple-choice—and is made up of questions that cover the key concepts in the selection. The Comprehension part

evaluates the student's ability to comprehend and apply theme skills to the authentic reading passage.

- **Word Skills:** This part consists of multiple-choice questions that assess the student's ability to apply word skills and decoding strategies taught in the theme to words and phrases in the test selection.

- **Writing and Language:** This part of the Integrated Theme Tests assesses the ability of the students to express themselves in writing. Students are given two prompts to choose from. The prompts are related to the reading but do not require that the students comprehend the reading selection in order to respond.

Because understanding of all instructed writing skills may not be evident in students' responses to the writing prompt, the Language part of the Integrated Theme Tests specifically tests the writing, spelling, and grammar skills taught in the theme. This section consists of a proofreading exercise and two additional writing skills questions.

- **Self-Assessment:** Concluding each Integrated Theme Test is an optional Self-Assessment activity. This activity encourages students to reflect on what they have read and what they have learned throughout the theme. By completing this self-evaluation activity at the end of each test, students provide information about their reading attitudes and habits and about their own perception of their growth as readers.

ADMINISTERING THE INTEGRATED THEME TESTS

Administer each Integrated Theme Test after students have read the corresponding theme in the Anthology, and after all skill and strategy instruction is complete.

Grouping

The Integrated Theme Tests are designed to be group administered, with students reading and responding individually at their own pace. However, depending on classroom needs, you may wish to administer the test to small groups or individual students.

Pacing

Most students will be able to complete each test in about one hour. Allow enough time for students to finish the test without rushing. Many teachers prefer to give the test in two sittings of 30–40 minutes on successive days, giving the test in sections as follows:
• Day 1: Comprehension and Word Skills
• Day 2: Writing and Language

Introducing the Test (Day 1)

These steps are suggested for introducing the test to students:
• Point out that the test offers an opportunity to read a selection related to the theme they have been studying.
• Read aloud the introduction that precedes the test selection.
• Explain what sections you expect students to complete in the first sitting.
• Assure students that after they read the selection, they can look back at the text as they answer the questions.
• Emphasize that you are interested in how well students read and understand the selection. Explain that they should do their best work but do not have to display perfect handwriting, spelling, and grammar.

• Point out that the multiple-choice questions have only one correct answer.

Introducing the Test (Day 2)

• Point out that in the second part of the test students will write about a topic related to the theme and will show what language skills they have learned.
• Allow students to choose one of the writing topics given in the test. Or, you may want to specify one of the topics or allow students to select their own topic related to the theme.
• Encourage students to spend a few minutes planning what they will write, following the planning process they typically use in your classroom.
• Explain to students that their writing is intended to be a first draft, but that they should do their best to express their ideas clearly and to use correct spelling and grammar. Encourage students to read over their work before they turn it in, checking to see that their writing makes sense and correcting spelling and grammar where possible.
• Some teachers may prefer to have students revise their writing as part of the test.
• You may want to review the proofreading marks found at the end of the *Literacy Activity Book* Student Handbook before students begin the proofreading section of the test.
• Tell students that while they will not be scored on the Self-Assessment part of the test, they should complete it to help them think about what they have learned in the theme. You may want to use their responses for a class discussion of the theme. Encourage them to take this section home to share with their families.

MEETING INDIVIDUAL NEEDS

By varying the amount of support you provide, you can adapt the Integrated Theme Tests to meet individual students' needs.

Working Independently

Most students will be able to complete the tests independently. They will do their best work if the test is given in a comfortable and supportive manner. The following steps will help establish this atmosphere:
- Read the test introduction aloud, addressing any questions before the students begin.
- During the test, circulate among the students, offering help if they have questions about what they are to do or need clarification about any of the test questions.
- Allow students time to finish the test without rushing.

Partial Support

For students who need a limited amount of support, use some or all of the following suggestions:
- Before students read the test selection, use the Prior Knowledge/Building Background activity on the Providing Support page, which is in the Teacher's Edition of each test.
- Give students the Purpose for Reading activity, which is also found on the Providing Support page.
- Allow students to read the selection independently or cooperatively with a partner.
- Coach students if they need help understanding questions or formulating their answers.

Full Support

For students who need more support, use the following suggestions:
- Use the Prior Knowledge/Building Background activity and the Purpose for Reading activity.
- Have students read the selection in sections, using the Guided Reading suggestions on the Providing Support page. Encourage students to then answer the test questions independently. If they need more help, have them answer the questions orally in the Guided Reading group, emphasizing the reasons for their answers.
- If some students need further support, have them work individually with you to answer the test questions orally.

Alternative Format

Even with the support suggested above, an occasional student may still have difficulty accessing test selections. In this case, you may wish to use the Alternative Format of the Integrated Theme Tests.

The Alternative Format Tests include a summary of the main test selection, written at a lower reading level, plus comprehension questions to be answered either orally or in writing, depending on students' abilities. The Alternative Format Tests can be administered individually or in a small group. They are provided as **blackline masters** in the back of this Teacher's Edition.

GUIDELINES FOR SCORING

Written-Response Questions (Scoring Using a Rubric)

A scoring rubric has been specifically designed for each open-ended question in the Integrated Theme Tests. Each rubric contains authentic sample answers, the score given for the answer, and the criterion used in determining this score. Each sample answer given is simply one example from a wide range of possible responses. (Note: Sample answers were chosen from student responses given during classroom field trials.) Because student approaches to the question will vary, the scoring criteria often suggest some different ways students may answer. Use your own interpretation of the reading to help you determine scores for answers that are different from the sample answers given. When scoring written-response questions, you should focus on the content and not be distracted by mechanics, spelling, or handwriting. Give a score of 0, 1, 2, 3, or 4 depending on your judgment of how many points a student's answer is worth.

Multiple-Choice Questions

Each multiple-choice item has only one correct answer. Students should fill in the circle next to the correct answer and leave the other three circles blank. In scoring these questions, give 1 point for each question that is answered correctly.

Writing

Students have the choice of two writing prompts. In evaluating student responses, more emphasis should be given to ideas, organization, and effective communication, and less to usage and mechanics. To score student responses, use the scoring rubric in the same manner as in scoring written comprehension questions. The rubric given in the Writing section is holistic and designed to apply to both writing prompts. The sample answers are representative of each score. Again, use both the rubric criteria and your own judgment to help you determine scores for answers that are different from the student samples.

Proofreading

The proofreading activity in each of the Integrated Theme Tests requires students to correct the grammar and spelling errors in the text given. Score student answers by giving one point to each item accurately corrected.

Self-Assessment

While there are no right or wrong answers to the questions in the Self-Assessment survey, students' responses are useful indicators of their progress in developing positive reading attitudes and habits and in evaluating their own growth as readers. Responses to the survey can best be evaluated holistically, considering the following questions:

- Does the student express clear opinions about what he or she has read? Do these opinions accurately reflect his or her attitudes about reading, based on what you already know?
- Does the student show interest in independent reading? Is there evidence of growth in this area?

DEVELOPING AND INTERPRETING STUDENT PROFILES

Recording Part Scores

Following each part in the student edition of the Integrated Theme Tests there is a score line to record the student's score for that part. Occasionally, the student's score must be multiplied by a given number. The score line is provided for your convenience in calculating the final score after the test has been completed. Transfer the part totals to the Student Profile on the test cover, recording the score for each part in the appropriate box.

Developing Student Profiles

After all part scores are recorded onto the Integrated Theme Test Record, you can develop the overall Student Profile by drawing a line connecting each part score.

After reviewing students' tests, you may wish to plan individual or small group conferences to discuss the test selection and test question responses. Information gathered in these conferences can be considered in making your overall evaluation of the students' test performances.

Interpreting Student Profiles

Students' performance on an Integrated Theme Test is one kind of evidence, but not the only kind of evidence, of their success. In making decisions about students' progress and needs, use the Integrated Theme Test results in combination with the information you have gathered from classroom observations and from such student work as the Reading-Writing Workshop and *Literacy Activity Book* activities.

Using an Integrated Theme Test to interpret student performance is best done by looking at the Student Profile and determining strengths and weaknesses. Review questions the student missed and look for patterns that may identify specific skill deficiencies.

Analyzing students' performance can often tell you how to help the student who is not performing well. This support can be provided as the student progresses through the program. After evaluating the tests, you may want to form a small group of students who exhibited similar difficulties on the test. Using the Integrated Theme Test as a basis for minilessons, review the test items the students missed, clarifying and discussing answers.

If the overall score or the score in one particular category is in the Needs Improvement range, you may wish to do further analysis to determine if placement is correct or if additional support is needed. You may want to use the Benchmark Progress Tests or the Informal Reading Inventory as an additional record of student progress.

PROVIDING ADDITIONAL SUPPORT

Here are some suggestions for following up on individual needs:

- If a student has difficulty with word skills, she or he may need individual or small-group instruction in decoding skills. The student may also benefit from reading and rereading of easier materials, such as titles listed in the *Teacher's Book*. In working on future themes, the student may benefit from teacher-directed reading or cooperative reading with students who have advanced decoding skills.

- If a student has difficulty with comprehension, be sure to give the student sufficient time to reread the selection. You might guide students through the reading if they have demonstrated significant difficulty. If a student is able to clarify his or her errors and demonstrate understanding of the questions missed, move on. If not, you may want to use the appropriate Reteaching lessons in the *Teacher's Book* or consult the Skill Finders in the *Teacher's Book* to determine the next time the skill will be addressed.

- If a student needs additional help in general comprehension, you might help her or him build understanding of the just-completed theme through discussion and explanation, individually or in small groups. For reading selections in future themes, the student may need more extensive building of background knowledge and vocabulary. The student may also benefit from cooperative or teacher-directed reading.

- If a student demonstrates difficulty in writing, you may provide more practice and support with writing. You might allow more time for writing and provide specific minilessons as needed. Use the students' Integrated Theme Tests to help them self-evaluate their writing. Discuss qualities of good writing and help them set goals for future writing.

In addition to providing information about a student who is not performing well, the Student Profile may also be used to indicate where further evaluation is redundant. For example, if you feel you already have enough information about your students' writing skills, you may decide that you do not need to administer the writing portion of every Integrated Theme Test. Other parts can be given to obtain useful information about your students' reading comprehension, word skills, and language skills.

Communicating with Parents

The optional Self-Assessment activity at the end of each Integrated Theme Test is in the form of a letter or poster that allows students to express their opinions of the theme and to assess their own work and learning. Students are encouraged to complete this activity and then share it with family members.

DEVELOPMENT OF THE INTEGRATED THEME TESTS

Reading selections for the Integrated Theme Tests were chosen by a team of educators, writers, and editors for the following characteristics:

- Topical interest and appeal to students
- Appropriate level for independent reading at each grade
- Relationship to the theme
- Reasonable length

Test questions were then developed by experienced, professional test writers. Each test included extra questions to allow for elimination of items that in field trials were found to be unclear or too difficult.

Classroom Field Trials

The Integrated Theme Tests underwent extensive classroom field trials to assure the accuracy and appropriateness of all questions. The field trials, conducted between January and May of 1995, involved more than 4,900 students. Each single Integrated Theme Test was tried out with between 160 and 200 students from urban, suburban, and rural schools in various regions of the United States. Results of the classroom trials were analyzed and scored by a team of experienced classroom teachers. Test items that were unclear, too difficult, or weak discriminators were eliminated. Student answers were used to develop scoring rubrics for all written-answer items. Tests were then rescored by different raters to establish inter-rater reliability and to assure consistency across each level of *Invitations to Literacy*.

Validity and Reliability

A technical report documenting the results of classroom field trials is available through your Houghton Mifflin representative.

OINK, OINK, OINK

LEVEL 3, THEME 1
Integrated Theme Test Record

Student _____ Date _____

STUDENT PROFILE					
	Part Scores:	**Excellent Progress**	**Good Progress**	**Some Progress**	**Needs Improve-ment**
Part 1: Reading Strategies •predict/infer	**Items 1–2**	7–8	5–6	3–4	0–2
Part 2: Comprehension •summarizing: story structure •compare and contrast •fantasy/realism	**Items 3–6 (written)**	14–16	11–13	7–10	0–6
	Items 7–11 (multiple-choice)	20	16	8–12	0–4
Part 3: Word Skills •base words •inflected forms •using context	**Items 12–17**	24	20	12–16	0–8
Part 4: Writing and Language Writing Fluency	**Item 18 Fluency**	20	15	10	0–5
Proofreading •short vowels, vowel-consonant-e, long *a* and long *e* •subjects and predicates, correcting run-on sentences, kinds of sentences	**Item 19 Language**	6	5	3–4	0–2
Writing Skills •writing a sentence •combining sentences: compound sentences	**Items 20–21 Writing Skills**	6		3	0
Part 5: Self-Assessment (optional) •self-assessment/reflection •developing preferences	**Home Letter**	Scoring of Self-Assessment is not recommended. Evaluate answers for evidence of metacognitive growth.			

Total Score
_____

☐ Excellent (90–100)
☐ Good (75–89)
☐ Satisfactory (60–74)
☐ Needs Improvement (0–59)

Additional Comments _____
_____
_____
_____

Test taken independently ☐
Test taken with partial support ☐
Test taken with full support ☐

PROVIDING SUPPORT

Most students should be able to take the test independently. For those needing more support, use the following suggestions.

Partial Support

• Use one or both of these activities before students read.

Prior Knowledge/Building Background

Use the following ideas to spark discussion about the selection:
• Ask students about other tales that they know.
• Ask students to think of ways that they could change other tales as the authors of the stories in Oink, Oink, Oink did.

Purpose for Reading

Have students read to find out what lesson the first and second little pigs learn.

• Allow students to read the selection cooperatively with a partner.
• Help students understand the questions and plan their answers.

Full Support

• Use **Prior Knowledge/Building Background** and **Purpose for Reading** activities above.
• **Guided Reading** Have students read the selection in sections. After each section, use the questions to guide students' reading:

Guided Reading

Section 1: From the beginning to the end of page 5
  Question: *Why does Papa Pig tell his sons to build a house out of bricks?*
Section 2: From page 6 to the end
  Question: *What happens when the first and second little pig do not listen to Papa Pig?*

• Encourage students to answer the test questions independently. If necessary, have them answer the questions orally in a group.
• For further support, have students work individually with you to answer the questions orally.

In Oink, Oink, Oink you read different versions of the old tale The Three Little Pigs. Now you will read another story about them. You will also read about real wolves.

Read the story and the article. There are questions to answer before, during, and after your reading. You may look back to the selections to help you answer the questions.

1 READING STRATEGIES

1. **Predict/Infer** Look at the title of the story and the pictures. Write what you think happens in this version of The Three Little Pigs.

Score	0	1	2	3	4
Criterion	Illegible or no answer	Makes an implausible or vague prediction	Makes a prediction based only on the original story	Makes a plausible prediction based on title and pictures	Makes a detailed prediction based upon title and pictures
Sample Answer		*I think a pig is getting a big opportunity.*	*I think the story is about three pigs and a wolf.*	*I think the story will about three pigs and their father. Similar to the three little pigs*	*I think the Papa wants his sons to build their houses and only one is a hard worker.*

Papa Pig and His Three Sons

Once there were three little pigs who lived in a big brick house with their father. One day, Papa Pig took his sons aside and said, "Now it's time for you to go out into the world and build houses of your own. But be careful of the big, bad wolf. When I was your age, the wolf would blow down a house made of straw or wood. So, take the time to build a strong and safe house out of bricks."

"But Dad!" said the first little pig, "That was in the old days. Things have changed."

"I don't know about that," said Papa Pig. "I know you think that I'm just being old-fashioned, but I'm warning you, the wolf is still dangerous."

The next day, the three little pigs went out to build their houses. The first little pig built his house out of straw, and the second little pig built his house out of wood. They were both finished in a few hours.

They quickly ran to visit the third little pig. But the third little pig was still building a house out of bricks.

"We're already done with our houses and you have barely started yours," the first and second little pigs bragged.

"We were told that we should build a strong and safe house and that's what I'm going to do," said the third little pig.

"What a nerd!" the first and second little pigs said. "Just because Dad told you to build a brick house doesn't mean you have to! Why don't you just build a house made of straw or wood like we did? Then you can come and play with us."

Then the third little pig said, "I am not a nerd! I just think Dad knows what he's talking about."

 Stop here and answer Question 2. Then continue reading.

READING STRATEGIES (continued)

2. **Predict/Infer** What do you think will happen in the rest of the story?

Score	0	1	2	3	4
Criterion	Illegible or no answer	Prediction is implausible or states a given fact	Prediction is plausible but not based on text	Gives general, logical prediction based on text	Gives specific prediction based on text
Sample Answer		*The first pig is going to build a house made out of straw*	*The first and second pig will get ate by the big bad wolf. And the third pig will eat the big, bad wolf.*	*I think the wolf will come and blow down their houses.*	*I think that after the third pig finishes the wolf will come and blow down the first and second pigs house.*

Rubric Score for Items 1–2 _____
8

"Fine. We're going fishing. Have fun working on your house," the two little pigs said. And they laughed all the way to the fishing pond.

While they were fishing, the big, bad wolf was lurking in the bushes. He was spying on the pigs. Suddenly, he ran out and tried to catch them. Luckily, the wolf was not a very fast runner. The pigs ran all the way to the straw house. They got there just in time to slam the door in his face.

"Little pigs, little pigs, let me come in," cried the wolf.

"Not by the hair of our chinny-chin-chins," said the pigs.

"Then I'll huff and I'll puff and I'll blow your house down," the wolf said.

And that's just what he did. So the two little pigs ran to the wood house. The wolf chased them, and again the pigs slammed the door in his face.

The wolf said, "Little pigs, little pigs, let me come in."

"Not by the hair of our chinny-chin-chins," the pigs replied.

So the wolf huffed and puffed and blew the wood house down.

This time, the pigs ran to Papa Pig's brick house where they were safe from the wolf. The wolf didn't even try to blow down the brick house. He knew he couldn't do it.

"I guess we should have listened to you," the first and second little pigs told their father. "We made houses of straw and wood, and the wolf blew them down."

The next day, the first and second little pigs went to see the third little pig. He was still working on his brick house.

"You were right to build a house out of bricks." said the first and second pigs. "Our houses weren't strong enough. Can we help you build your house?" they asked.

The third little pig agreed. They all built a strong and safe brick house. And they lived in it together, happily ever after.

You just read a story about an imaginary wolf. The article below tells about real wolves.

Wolf

from The World Book Encyclopedia, 1993

Wolves hunt at any time of the day or night. When the members of a pack gather to begin a hunt, they greet each other with howls. Their howling may become very loud, and it warns other wolves to stay out of the pack's territory.

Wolves roam through their territory until they find prey. They then choose a particular animal and move in on it by traveling toward it in the direction opposite that from which the wind is blowing. This method prevents the animal from smelling the wolves.

2 COMPREHENSION

Write your answers to these questions.

3. Why did the first and second little pigs make fun of the third little pig? *(comprehension/critical thinking)*

Score	0	1	2	3	4
Criterion	Illegible or no answer	Doesn't answer the question; may describe how the first and second little pigs made fun of the third little pig	Includes one plausible reason why the first and second little pigs made fun of the third little pig, but lacks detail	Includes with adequate detail one plausible reason why the first and second little pigs made fun of the third little pig	Includes with adequate detail more than one plausible reason why the first and second little pigs made fun of the third little pig
Sample Answer		Because they are mean and they build their houses out of bricks.	because he was building instead of playing.	The first and second pig made fun of the third pig because he was building his house out of bricks like their father.	The first and second little pigs made fun of the third pig because he was making a brick house. And he was taking his time to make it but his brothers didn't they made a straw and wood house.

4. How is the first pig's house different from the third pig's house? *(compare and contrast)*

Score	0	1	2	3	4
Criterion	Illegible or no answer	Inaccurate	Describes only one of the houses; may talk about both houses but not contrast them	Includes at least one contrast between the two houses	Includes at least two contrasts between the two houses; may include types of materials used, strength of the houses, time taken to build houses, and safety of the houses
Sample Answer		the second pig built a wimpy house.	The first pig's house was made of straw.	The first pigs house is made out of straw. And the third pig's house is made out of Brick	The first pigs house is made of straw not strong-and the third pig house is made of bricks strong.

5. Write a short summary of the selection "Wolf."
(summarizing: story structure)

Score	0	1	2	3	4
Criterion	Illegible or no answer	Inaccurate or mentions irrelevant information	Gives details from the selection but leaves out main ideas; may repeat the selection verbatim	Includes some main ideas but may leave out some important information	Summary is clear; includes main ideas of the selection
Sample Answer		*you should never stand in a wolves territory or the wolves will eat you. The wolves howl to greet each other.*	*The story Wolf is about real wolves. They hunt at night or they hunt daily. They greet each other by howling and that also warns other packs to stay far away.*	*Wolves hunt at any time. A pack greets each other with howling if it becomes loud it warns others to stay away to get prey they travel in the opposite direction of the wind.*	*Wolves hunt whenever they want to. They come together in a group and greet one another with howls. When they find prey, they go to it the opposite way the wind is blowing, so that the prey will not smell it.*

6. How is the wolf in "Papa Pig and His Three Sons" like a real wolf? How is he different? Give at least one similarity and one difference. *(fantasy/realism)*

Score	0	1	2	3	4
Criterion	Illegible or no answer	Attempts an answer, but response does not make sense; may give a detail from either selection	Gives either a similarity or a difference; or gives both a similarity and a difference but it is not clear which is which	Gives one similarity and one difference and says which is which	Gives more than one similarity or difference and identifies which are which
Sample Answer		*Wolf hunt in a pack*	*The wolf in the story hunted for food just like real wolves do.*	*He is real because he was looking for prey. He is different because he was not with a pack looking for prey.*	*He's like real wolves because he eats meat, he chases animals, and he hunts any time. He is different because he talks, and he blows houses down.*

Rubric Score for Items 3–6 _____

16

Choose the best answer and fill in the circle.

7. How is Papa Pig's house different from the first little pig's house? *(compare and contrast)*

    ● a. Papa Pig's house is big and strong.
    ○ b. Papa Pig's house has a flower garden.
    ○ c. Papa Pig's house is new.
    ○ d. Papa Pig's house is painted yellow.

8. Why didn't the first little pig build a house out of bricks? *(comprehension/critical thinking)*

    ● a. He didn't want to take the time to build a brick house.
    ○ b. His dad already had a brick house.
    ○ c. He thinks his dad knows what he is talking about.
    ○ d. He thinks straw houses are prettier.

9. How was the third little pig different from his brothers? *(compare and contrast)*

    ○ a. He did not like to go fishing.
    ○ b. He built a house of sticks.
    ○ c. He did not want to work hard.
    ● d. He did what Papa Pig told him to do.

10. Why couldn't the wolf in "Papa Pig and His Three Sons" catch the pigs? *(summarizing: story structure)*

- ○ a. The wolf let them get away.
- ● b. The wolf is not a very fast runner.
- ○ c. The pigs tricked the wolf.
- ○ d. The pigs tripped the wolf.

11. How do real wolves trick their prey? *(fantasy/realism)*

- ● a. They make sure the prey can't smell them.
- ○ b. They pretend they're sleeping.
- ○ c. They build traps for their prey.
- ○ d. They put on a disguise.

Score for Items 7–11 (x4) _____

20

3 WORD SKILLS

Read the sentence or sentences. Use what you know about figuring out new words to help you select the correct answer.

12. *We're going <u>fishing</u>.*

    What were they going to do? *(base words)*
    - ○ a. They were going to sew.
    - ● b. They were going to fish.
    - ○ c. They were going to run.
    - ○ d. They were going to climb a tree.

13. *The big bad wolf was <u>lurking</u> in the bushes. He was spying on the pigs.*

    What was the big bad wolf doing in the bushes? *(think about words)*
    - ○ a. sleeping
    - ○ b. playing cards
    - ● c. waiting
    - ○ d. eating

14. *The pigs <u>slammed</u> the door in his face.*

    What did the pigs do? *(inflected form -ed)*
    - ○ a. painted the door
    - ● b. shut the door loudly
    - ○ c. opened the door
    - ○ d. closed the door quietly

15. *When the members of a pack gather to begin a hunt, they greet each other with howls.*

Which of the following best describes a pack? *(using context)*
- ○ a. something to carry books in
- ○ b. putting things in a suitcase
- ○ c. a club
- ● d. a group of wolves or other animals

16. *Their howling may become very loud, and it warns other wolves to stay out of the pack's territory.*

How do the wolves greet each other? *(using context)*
- ○ a. by looking at each other
- ● b. by making noises
- ○ c. by walking in a circle
- ○ d. by rolling on the ground

17. *This method prevents the animal from smelling the wolves.*

What is prevented? *(inflected form -ing)*
- ● a. animals using their sense of smell
- ○ b. animals having a bad odor
- ○ c. animals finding trouble
- ○ d. animals swimming

Score for Items 12–17 (x4) _____

24

4 WRITING AND LANGUAGE

18. Write one or two paragraphs about one of the topics below.

   a. If you could build your own house, what would it be like? Describe it carefully.

   b. The first little pig learned from his mistake. Tell about a time when you learned a lesson from your mistake.

Scoring Rubric

Score	0	1	2	3	4
Criteria	illegible, no answer, or not related to prompt	•has no clear topic, or topic only vaguely relates to prompt •has little or no organization •has little or no use of details to explain reasoning behind answer •has limited or immature word choice •has major grammar, spelling, and mechanics errors	•states topic, but may include unrelated ideas; may address both prompts •uses an organizational pattern with lapses •details to explain reasoning are not fully developed •has adequate word choice, not always precise •contains many grammar, spelling, and mechanics errors	•states topic clearly, and generally stays on subject •uses an organizational pattern with few lapses •uses adequate supporting details, but some may be irrelevant •has adequately precise word choice •contains a few grammar, spelling, and mechanics errors *or* •might have rated a 4 except for significant grammar, spelling, and mechanics errors	•focuses on topic throughout •uses a clear, consistent organizational pattern •uses many relevant supporting details to explain reasoning behind answer •usually precise and creative in word choice •contains few grammar, spelling, and mechanics errors

On the following pages you will find sample student responses for Question 18.

Rubric Score for Item 18 (x5) _____
                                       20

Anchor Papers: *Sample Responses for Question 18 (Prompt a)*

Score 4: *This response has a clear topic, and the writer focuses on this topic. There is good organization as the writer takes the reader through each part of the house. The writer uses descriptive language. There are few grammar, spelling, and mechanics errors.*

My dreamhouse would be a two story I would have 4 bedrooms upstairs and 1 bathroom and downstairs I would have 1 bathroom a family room, dining room McDonalds and a kitchen. The color would be white with a two pink doors. In the back I would have a pool and a spa and shady trees with a garden.

My dreamhouse would be a two story I would have 4 bedrooms upstairs and 1 bathroome and downstairs I would have 1 bathroom a family room, dinning room Mc domdlds and a kicthen. The color would be white with a two pink dooos. In the back I woud have a pool and a spea and shady trees. with a garden.

Score 3: *This response shows an understanding of the prompt. It tells the reader how the house will be designed but not how the house will look. The word choice is adequate, but it is not very descriptive. The response contains a few grammar, spelling, and mechanics errors.*

On my house I would like four windows one in the kitchen, one in my room, one big window in the living room, and one in the garage. I'll have two bathrooms one in my room and one in the hall. I will have my house up in the mountains. And I will have two bedrooms.

On my house -. I would like four windows one in the kechten, one in my room, one big window in the living room, and one in the garage. Ill have two bathrooms one in my room and one in the hall. I will have my house up in the momtasns. And I will have two bedrooms.

Anchor Papers: *Sample Responses for Question 18 (Prompt a)*

Score 2: *This response states the topic, but it does not develop the topic beyond basic ideas. The writing is simple.*

If I could build my own house it would be big. It would be made of bricks and it would be safe from everything.	If I could build my own house it would be big. It would be made of bricks and it would be safe from everything.

Score 1: *This response is vague and lacks originality.*

If I could build my own house it would be like the third little pigs house in the story at the beginning.	If I could build my own house it would be like the third little pigs house in the story at the beging.

Anchor Papers: *Sample Responses for Question 18 (Prompt b)*

Score 4: *The writer states what the mistake was and tells about that mistake. The writer creates excitement by describing the effects of the mistake and the sprint through the house. At the end, the writer states specifically what lesson was learned.*

I learned from a mistake by putting a metal key in a plug in. When the key was in I got electrocuted and my whole foot turned black. After that I ran from where I was, which was the last room in my house to the first room in my house in about three seconds. The lesson I learned was to never stick a metal item like a key or another item in a plug in.

> I learned from a mistake by puting a motel key in a plug in When the key was in I got electrocuted and my hole foot turned black. After that I ran from were I was which was the last room in my house to the first room in my house in about three seconds. The lesson I learned was to never stick a metal item like a key or another item in a plug in.

Score 3: *This response sometimes strays from the main topic. While the mistake is mentioned, the writer only hints at the lesson learned but does not state it explicitly. The word choice is adequate to describe the event, but it does not do anything to make the story more interesting. There are some grammar, spelling, and mechanics mistakes.*

I learned from my mistake when I broke my neighbors window. I didn't want to tell my mother but she noticed. My mom was very mad at me. I went on my bike and went around the block. Then my dad came home and was mad at me, too. Then my neighbor came home and wasn't mad at me. I was lucky. But I didn't have to pay for the window, my dad did. Then I tried not to break a window again. Then I went on playing a game, but not golfing, a funner game.

> I learned from my mistake when I brok my neibers window. I didn't wantto tell my mother but she noticed. My mom was very mad at me. I went on my bike and went around the block. Then my dad came home and was mad at me too. Then my neiber came home and wasn't mad at me. I was lucky. But I didn't have to pay for the window, my dad did. Then I tried not to breck a window agian. Then I went on playing a game. but not golfing, a funner game.

Anchor Papers: *Sample Responses for Question 18 (Prompt b)*

Score 2: *This response answers only part of the prompt. It does not say what happened that caused the lesson to be learned.*

When I throw a piece of metal at a car my lesson was never throw things at cars. If you do you can get into a lot of trouble. I did. You should not throw something at another thing.

When I throw a piece of medal at acar my lessen wos never throw things at cars. If you do you can get into a lot of trouble I did You should not throw some thing at a nother thing.

Score 1: *This response answers only a small part of the prompt. It does not state what lesson was learned or why a lesson was learned. There are many spelling errors.*

My mistake was putting a crayon in my ear when I was five.

my mistek wis pateing a cran in my ear win Iwis 5

19. Read the article below. Find and correct six errors. Use what you know about proofreading to make your corrections in the article. The examples may help you. There are four errors in subjects and predicates, run-on sentences, and kinds of sentences. There are also two spelling errors.

(subjects and predicates, correcting run-on sentences, kinds of sentences, short vowels, vowel-consonant-e, long a and long e)

From Caves to Houses

People ~~nede~~ *need* places to live. Many years ago, people *lived* in caves. The caves gav*e* them dry places to sleep. The caves also helped keep people safe from wild animals.

Over time, *people* began to build houses. People who lived near forests built houses of logs. people who lived in dry places built houses of clay. Some people *built* houses from dried ~~grais~~ *grass*.

Base each student's score on the number of errors found and corrected, not on the student's use of proofreading marks. You may wish to refer students to the proofreading marks at the end of the Literacy Activity Book Student Handbook.

Score for Item 19 _____
6

Fill in the circle next to the complete sentence. *(writing a sentence)*

20. ● a. The pigs built a brick house.
    ○ b. A brick house
    ○ c. The big bad wolf
    ○ d. Built a brick house

Combine the two sentences to make a compound sentence. *(combining sentences: compound sentences)*

21. The pigs fished. The wolf watched from the bushes.

The pigs fished, and the wolf watched from the bushes.

Score for Items 20–21 (x3) _____
6

5 Self-Assessment (optional)
HOME LETTER

Complete the letter below. There are no right or wrong answers, but your answers should show that you have thought about what you have read.

Dear _____ ,

My favorite story in Oink, Oink, Oink was _____

_____.

If I could be one of the characters I read about, I'd be

_____ because

_____.

One thing I learned was _____

_____

_____.

Some new words I learned were _____

_____.

Sincerely,

_____

COMMUNITY TIES

LEVEL 3, THEME 2

Integrated Theme Test Record

Student _____ Date _____

STUDENT PROFILE					
	Part Scores:	Excellent Progress	Good Progress	Some Progress	Needs Improvement
Part 1: Reading Strategies •predict/infer •evaluate	Items 1–2	7–8	5–6	3–4	0–2
Part 2: Comprehension •noting details •author's viewpoint •making generalizations	Items 3–6 (written)	14–16	11–13	7–10	0–6
	Items 7–11 (multiple-choice)	20	16	8–12	0–4
Part 3: Word Skills •plurals •compound words •contractions	Items 12–17	24	20	12–16	0–8
Part 4: Writing and Language Writing Fluency	Item 18 Fluency	20	15	10	0–5
Proofreading •long *i* and long *o*, vowel sound in *knew*, vowel sound in *town* •singular and plural nouns, singular and plural possessive nouns, common and proper nouns	Item 19 Language	6	5	3–4	0–2
Writing Skills •combining sentences: compound subjects	Items 20–21 Writing Skills	6		3	0
Part 5: Self-Assessment (optional) •self-assessment/reflection •developing preferences	Home Letter	Scoring of Self-Assessment is not recommended. Evaluate answers for evidence of metacognitive growth.			

Total Score

_____

☐ **Excellent (90–100)**
☐ **Good (75–89)**
☐ **Satisfactory (60–74)**
☐ **Needs Improvement (0–59)**

Additional Comments _____

_____

_____

_____

Test taken independently ☐

Test taken with partial support ☐

Test taken with full support ☐

PROVIDING SUPPORT

Most students should be able to take the test independently. For those needing more support, use the following suggestions.

Partial Support

- Use one or both of these activities before students read:

Prior Knowledge/Building Background

Use the following ideas to spark discussion about the selection:

- Ask students to describe some of the stores they shop in. What things are for sale in those stores? What do the people who work in the stores do?
- Ask students where people get together to have fun in their community. Have them describe what people do in these places.

Purpose for Reading

Have students read to find out what life is like in a country store.

- Allow students to read the selection cooperatively with a partner.
- Help students understand the questions and plan their answers.

Full Support

- Use **Prior Knowledge/Building Background** and **Purpose for Reading** activities above.
- **Guided Reading** Have students read the selection in sections. After each section, use the questions to guide students' reading:

Guided Reading

Section 1: From the beginning to the middle of page 24
   Question: *What are some things the owners of the store do at their store?*
Section 2: From the middle of page 24 to the end
   Question: *What do the people who visit the store do when they are there?*

- Encourage students to answer the test questions independently. If necessary, have them answer the questions orally in a group.
- For further support, have students work individually with you to answer the questions orally.

Community Ties

In Community Ties you read about different communities and how the people in each of these communities live together.

Now you will read a story about a family that runs a country store. Following the story is an article about kids who run a different kind of store.

There are questions to answer before, during, and after your reading. You may go back to the selections to help you answer the questions.

1 READING STRATEGIES

1. **Predict/Infer** Before you read the first story, look at the titles and pictures. What do you think the story will be about?

Score	0	1	2	3	4
Criterion	Illegible or no answer	Makes implausible or vague prediction	Makes a limited prediction based only on title or one or two pictures	Makes a plausible but general prediction	Makes a specific, detailed prediction
Sample Answer		*They get really rich*	*about a store*	*I think the story will be about a family that runs a store*	*I think it will be about a family who runs a nice store in the country with a big house.*

We Keep a Store

by Anne Shelby

We keep a store. It sits right in our front yard, so whenever we need anything all we have to do is walk across the yard to the store and get it.

We don't even have to pay ourselves for it. That's one good thing about keeping a store.

In a corner behind the counter there's a cardboard box. When a customer wants candy, my mother scoops a scoop into the box and comes up with gum drops, lemon drops, and creams.

She slides the candy into a paper sack and weighs it on the big white scale. Sometimes she has to take a little out or put a few more pieces in.

When she isn't looking I can eat a piece of candy right out of that box. That's another good thing about keeping a store.

My mother figures out what to order from the big grocery company.

When the truck comes, my father slits the boxes open with his knife. I help stack cans on shelves.

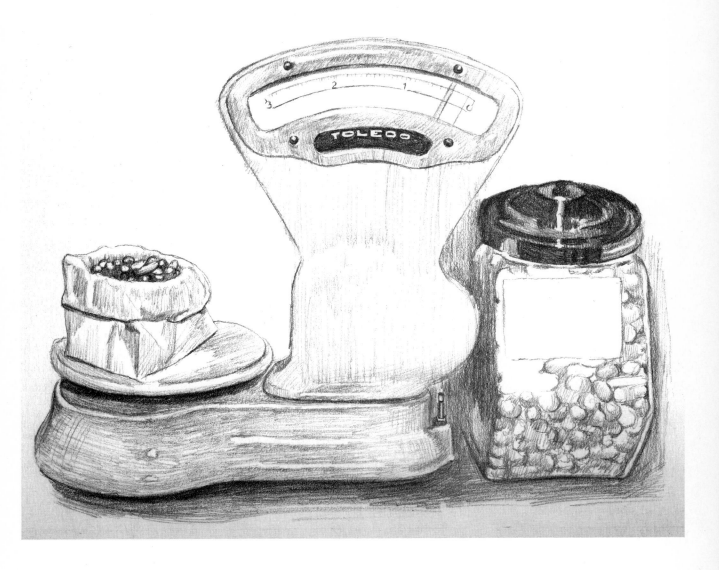

We all wait on customers and put money in the cash register and count out change.

We work together. That's another good thing about keeping a store.

But our customers don't come just to buy things. They come to visit, too.

In winter, the men circle their chairs around the stove and tell long stories about the old days when wolves and bears and foxes roamed the country.

In summer, they move their chairs outside and whittle till curls of cedar shavings pile up around their shoes.

The women sit with my mother under the apple trees in the yard. They help her string green beans to can or cut apples up to dry.

Their children play with me in the field beside the store. We play kick-the-can or hide-and-go-seek or something we just make up, like chase-that-chicken or see-who's-the-first-to-fall-into-the-creek.

Finally, toward dark, a grown-up hollers for the children to come on, it's time to go home.

"You all come back," my father tells them. And they answer, "We'll be back."

They mean it, too. That's the best thing about keeping a store.

 Stop here and answer Question 2. Then continue reading.

READING STRATEGIES (continued)

2. **Evaluate** Do you think this might be a true story? Why or why not?

Score	0	1	2	3	4
Criterion	Illegible or no answer	Responds yes or no, but gives no explanation	Responds yes or no; gives vague explanation	Responds yes or no, and gives 1 supporting detail or example	Responds yes or no, and gives more than 1 clear supporting detail and/or example
Sample Answer		*Yes*	*Yes, because it sound very real.*	*yes because some people own stores*	*Yes, because some things they do in stories they do in real life, like run a store, play hide and go seek, chase, the chicken, or freeze tag.*

Rubric Score for Items 1–2 _____

8

Now read this article about a different kind of store — a bookstore in a New York City school.

The Children's Bookstore

from *Kid City* magazine

Students at P.S. 121 in the Bronx are learning how to be sales people, cashiers, and business owners — plus they're reading and having fun! They have started their own school bookstore. It all began when one teacher let her students borrow books, like a library. She noticed a lot of the kids were not returning the books — they wanted to keep them!

Now students at the school run the bookstore. Some kids work as cashiers. Others read books and write reviews to tell other kids what's good. The kids are "paid" with coupons for free books. They love their jobs and they love reading. "If I ever stopped reading," said one student, "I don't know what would happen to me!"

2 COMPREHENSION

Write your answers to these questions.

3. In what way does the girl help out in *We Keep a Store*? *(noting details)*

Score	0	1	2	3	4
Criterion	Illegible or no answer	Inaccurate, vague, or refers to second selection	States that she helps her mother and father, but doesn't mention specific ways	Describes one of the ways in which she helps	Describes more than 1 of the ways in which she helps
Sample Answer		*She helps her mom with the sweets.*	*The girl helped in the store by working together.*	*She helps stack the cans on the shelves.*	*The girl helps by stacking cans on shelves, and putting money in the cash register and count out change*

4. Why do you think the father tells the people to come back? *(comprehension/critical thinking)*

Score	0	1	2	3	4
Criterion	Illegible or no answer	Inaccurate; may restate what father says	Vague; may state reason not supported by the story	Gives one logical reason that is based on evidence from the story	Gives two or more reasons that are based on evidence from the story
Sample Answer		*Because it was getting dark*	*He tells the people to come because so they'll come back*	*I think the father tells the people to come back again because he would like to see them again.*	*He wants them to come back because he wanted them to visit him and family, buy things from the store.*

5. How do you think the author of *We Keep a Store* feels about the country store? Explain your answer. *(author's viewpoint)*

Score	0	1	2	3	4
Criterion	Illegible or no answer	Inaccurate; does not state the author's opinion about the store	States how the author feels, but gives no explanation	States how the author feels and gives example of evidence to support that statement	States how the author feels and gives specific evidence from the text to support that statement
Sample Answer		*I think the author likes the story*	*good!*	*I think they might like it because they wrote the story.*	*Probably good because the story tells what is good about running a store*

6. You read about two different kinds of stores. Do you think it is easy or hard to run a store? Explain your answer. *(making generalizations)*

Score	0	1	2	3	4
Criterion	Illegible or no answer	Inaccurate or vague; may not state opinion	States opinion with no explanation	States opinion and gives general explanation	States opinion; cites specific examples from the text and from personal experience in the explanation
Sample Answer		*it was fun reading "We Keep a Store" because it is fun when the girl plays.*	*I just don't think it would be hard.*	*I think it's kind of hard because there's a bunch of stuff to do when you are keeping a store.*	*I think it is hard to run a store because you have to stack everything and you have to make sure everything is in its right place.*

Rubric Score for Items 3–6 _____

16

Read each question. Fill in the circle next to the correct answer.

7. What do the customers who visit the country store
    do there? *(noting details)*

    ○ a. They open boxes.
    ○ b. They wait on customers.
    ● c. They buy candy.
    ○ d. They never come back.

8. What do the men do when they come to
    the store? *(noting details)*

    ○ a. They play kick-the-can.
    ● b. They tell stories.
    ○ c. They cut apples.
    ○ d. They sit around the stove during the summer.

9. Which sentence best describes the owners of the
    country store? *(making generalizations)*

    ○ a. They are quiet and shy.
    ○ b. They always have people in their house.
    ○ c. They do not like to pay for things.
    ● d. They are friendly and helpful.

10. Why did the kids in "The Children's Bookstore" want to keep the books that they borrowed from their teacher? *(comprehension/critical thinking)*

- ○ a. They liked working in the bookstore.
- ○ b. The books were new.
- ● c. The kids loved to read.
- ○ d. Their teacher told them they could keep the books.

11. Which sentence describes how the writer of "The Children's Bookstore" feels about kids running their own business? *(author's viewpoint)*

- ● a. It's a good idea because they will learn a lot.
- ○ b. They are too young to run their own business.
- ○ c. They should not run a business because they might stop reading.
- ○ d. They would do better selling lemonade.

Score for Items 7–11 (x4) _____
20

3 WORD SKILLS

Read the sentence or sentences. Use what you know about figuring out new words to help you select the correct answer.

12. *We <u>don't</u> even have to pay ourselves for it.*

What does *don't* mean? *(contractions)*
- ○ a. does not
- ● b. do not
- ○ c. do nothing
- ○ d. do never

13. *In a corner behind the counter there's a <u>cardboard</u> box.*

Which is the best description of the box? *(compound words)*
- ○ a. It is large enough to hold a deck of cards.
- ● b. It is made from material that is stiff like a card.
- ○ c. It is made from a board used in a card game.
- ○ d. It is made from greeting cards.

14. *When she isn't looking I can eat a piece of <u>candy</u> right out of that box.*

If you had many pieces of candy, what would you have? *(plurals)*
- ○ a. many candys
- ○ b. many candyes
- ○ c. many candis
- ● d. many candies

15. *When the truck comes, my father <u>slits</u> the boxes open with his knife.*

What does the father do to the boxes? *(think about words)*

○ a. He tears them open.
○ b. He pulls them open.
● c. He makes long, narrow cuts in them.
○ d. He stacks the cans on the shelves.

16. *Students at P.S. 121 in the Bronx are learning how to be sales people, cashiers, and business owners — plus they're reading and having fun! They have started their own school <u>bookstore</u>.*

What have the students at P.S. 121 done? *(compound words)*

○ a. They have made a place where people can store their extra books.
○ b. They have built a piece of furniture where people can put books.
● c. They have begun a store where people can buy books.
○ d. They have filled their school with many books.

17. *The kids are "paid" with <u>coupons</u> for free books.*

With what are the kids "paid"? *(think about words)*

○ a. free passes to go sit on a chicken's house
○ b. coins and dollar bills
○ c. chances to do other jobs in the bookstore
● d. tickets that let them get free books

Score for Items 12–17 (x4) _____
24

4 WRITING AND LANGUAGE

18. Write one or two paragraphs about one of the topics below.

a. Write about a special place in your community that you like to visit with your family or friends. Explain why you like to go there.

b. The students that work in the school bookstore love their job. Tell about the kind of job you would like to do in your school or neighborhood.

Scoring Rubric

Score	0	1	2	3	4
Criteria	illegible, no answer, or not related to prompt	•has no clear topic, or topic only vaguely relates to prompt •has little or no organization •has little or no use of details to explain reasoning behind answer •has limited or immature word choice •has major grammar, spelling, and mechanics errors	•states topic, but may include unrelated ideas; may address both prompts •uses an organizational pattern with lapses •details to explain reasoning are not fully developed •has adequate word choice, not always precise •contains many grammar, spelling, and mechanics errors	•states topic clearly, and generally stays on subject •uses an organizational pattern with few lapses •uses adequate supporting details, but some may be irrelevant •has adequately precise word choice •contains a few grammar, spelling, and mechanics errors or •might have rated a 4 except for significant grammar, spelling, and mechanics errors	•focuses on topic throughout •uses a clear, consistent organizational pattern •uses many relevant supporting details to explain reasoning behind answer •usually precise and creative in word choice •contains few grammar, spelling, and mechanics errors

On the following pages you will find sample student responses for Question 18.

Rubric Score for Item 18 (x5) _____
20

Anchor Papers: *Sample Responses for Question 18 (Prompt a)*

Score 4: *This response focuses on the prompt. The writing follows a clear pattern and includes interesting details and vocabulary. There are almost no errors in grammar, spelling, and mechanics.*

I like to go to my grandma's house. I like to go to her house because she's nice, and helpful, and also caring. Every time I go there we play games and I get popsicles. That is the reason I like to go to her house.

> I like to go to my grandma's house. I like to go to her house because she's nice, and helpful, and also caring. Every time I go their we play games and I get pop cicles. That is the reason I like to go to her house.

Score 3: *The writer gives a clear response about a special place to go with family. The answer is clearly organized and detailed and includes adequate vocabulary to express the writer's ideas. This response would have rated a 4 except for significant grammar, spelling, and mechanics errors.*

I Like to go to the gardens with my family because I like the plants and I try to guess the name of plants. Sometimes I quiz my Aunt, like I will see a evergreen and ask my aunt what is that and sometimes she will play and say I don't know what is it.

> I Like to go to the gardens with my family because, I like the plants and I try to geus. the name of plants. Some times I ques my Aunt, like I will See a evergreen a d ack my aunt what is that und sometimes she will play and Say I don't Knok what is it.

Anchor Papers: *Sample Responses for Question 18 (Prompt a)*

Score 2: *This response answers only part of the prompt. It does not describe the special place, nor does it go into any detail about why the writer and his or her family have a good time there. The word choice is basic. There are no grammar, spelling, and mechanics errors.*

I like to go to the mountains because I have a good time with my family.

> I like to go to the mountains because I have a good time with my family.

Score 1: *This response answers only part of the prompt.*

I like to go to school because We learn.

> I like to go to school because We learn.

Anchor Papers: *Sample Responses for Question 18 (Prompt b)*

Score 4: *This response focuses on the prompt. It is well organized, with introductory and closing sentences. The writer provides detail to support the topic. The word choice is adequate. There are few errors in grammar, spelling, and mechanics.*

I would like to work a lemonade stand. I would say that the lemonade was 25¢ a cup, I would only work in the summer. I would make it out of fresh lemons. The people would love it.

> I would like to work a limonade stand. I would say that the limonade was 25¢ a cup, I would only work in the summer. I would make it out of fresh limons. The people would love it.

Score 3: *This response focuses on the topic. It shows a clear organizational pattern. The writer does not know the term* cashier *and so incorrectly uses the term* cash register. *There are few grammar, spelling, and mechanics errors.*

The kind of job I would like to have is being a cash register because it is kind of fun to me. I would also like to be a cash register so I could get paid and help people with their groceries.

> The kind of job I would like to have is being a cash register because it is kind of fun to me. I would also like to he a cash register so I could get paid and help people with their groceries.

Anchor Papers: *Sample Responses for Question 18 (Prompt b)*

Score 2: *The response answers the prompt, but it does not give any supporting details. The writer strays from the topic in the second and third sentences. Also, the answer is based upon "The Children's Bookstore" instead of being based upon the writer's own ideas. There are many grammar, spelling, and mechanics errors.*

I would like to sale books in school because that seems fun. Like one day half the class could sale. Then the other half could.

> I would like to sale books in school because that simes fun. Like one day have the class could sale. Then the other half could.

Score 1: *This response tells what kind of job the writer would like but not why. It contains multiple grammar, spelling, and mechanics errors.*

I would like to pick up trash.

> I woull lick to pick up trach

19. **Read the advertisement below. Find and correct six errors. Use what you know about proofreading to make your corrections in the advertisement. The examples may help you. There are two spelling errors and four errors in nouns.**

(long i and long o, the vowel sound in knew, *the vowel sound in* town, *singular and plural nouns, singular and plural possessive nouns, common and proper nouns)*

Two neighborhood third graders want work!

We kno͠w our work, and we do͠ it well. Here are some of

the jobs we have done so far:

We raked ~~leafs~~ leaves at Jimmy Smith's house.

We watched Mrs. Carter's dog while she

was out of ~~toun~~ town.

We taught three child͠ren how to fly a kite.

We set up chairs for the community

Fourth of july parade.

Call us at 555–1234 if you want the job done ~~rite~~ right. We

hope you will give us a try!

Becky and Conchita

Base each student's score on the number of errors found and corrected, not on the student's use of proofreading marks. You may wish to refer students to the proofreading marks at the end of the Literacy Activity Book *Student Handbook.*

Score for Item 19 _____
6

Combine each pair of sentences below by using compound subjects. *(combining sentences: compound subjects)*

20. Becky wrote an ad. Rachel wrote an ad.

Becky and Rachel wrote an ad.

_____

_____

_____

_____

_____

21. The children painted the school. The teachers painted the school. *(combining sentences: compound subjects)*

The children and the teachers painted the school.

_____

_____

_____

_____

_____

Score for Items 20–21 (x3) _____

6

Self-Assessment (optional)

HOME LETTER

Theme Selections

A Fruit & Vegetable Man
Family Pictures/Cuadros de familia
When Jo Louis Won the Title

Write a letter to a friend or family member. Your letter should show that you have thought about what you have read.

Date _____

Dear _____ ,

   I just finished reading Community Ties. All of the stories are about different communities and the people who live and work in them.

   Of all the characters I read about in Community Ties, the character that is most like me is

_____ .

   This character is most like me because

_____

_____ .

   The most important thing I learned about belonging to a community is

_____

_____ .

           Sincerely,

           _____

DISASTER!

LEVEL 3, THEME 3

Integrated Theme Test Record

Student _____ Date _____

STUDENT PROFILE					
	Part Scores:	Excellent Progress	Good Progress	Satis-factory Progress	Needs Improve-ment
Part 1: Reading Strategies •self-question •predict/infer	Items 1–2	7–8	5–6	3–4	0–2
Part 2: Comprehension •topic/main idea/supporting details •fact and opinion •cause and effect	Items 3–6 (written)	14–16	11–13	7–10	0–6
	Items 7–11 (multiple-choice)	20	16	8–12	0–4
Part 3: Word Skills •word endings •syllabication •synonyms	Items 12–17	24	20	12–16	0–8
Part 4: Writing and Language Writing Fluency	Item 18 Fluency	20	15	10	0–5
Proofreading •vowel sound in *saw* and vowel + *r* sounds •verbs in the present, verbs in the past, the verb *be*	Item 19 Language	6	5	3–4	0–2
Writing Skills •combining sentences: compound predicates	Items 20–21 Writing Skills	6		3	0
Part 5: Self-Assessment (optional) •self-reflection/assessment •developing preferences	Home Letter	Scoring of Self-Assessment is not recommended. Evaluate answers for evidence of metacognitive growth.			

Total Score _____	☐ **Excellent (90–100)** ☐ **Good (75–89)** ☐ **Satisfactory (60–74)** ☐ **Needs Improvement (0–59)**

Additional Comments _____

_____

_____

_____

Test taken independently ☐

Test taken with partial support ☐

Test taken with full support ☐

PROVIDING SUPPORT

Most students should be able to take the test independently. For those needing more support use the following suggestions.

Partial Support

- Use one or both of these activities before students read.

Prior Knowledge/Building Background

Use the following ideas to spark discussion about the selection:

- Ask students what they learned from reading the main selections of Disaster!
- Ask students if they know about any other disasters in history. Have them tell the class what they know about these disasters.

Purpose for Reading

Have students read to learn more about the destruction caused by the Great San Francisco Earthquake.

- Allow students to read the selection cooperatively with a partner.
- Help students understand the questions and plan their answers.

Full Support

- Use the **Prior Knowledge/Building Background** and **Purpose for Reading** activities above.
- **Guided Reading** Have students read the selection in sections. After each section, use the questions below to guide students' reading.

Guided Reading

Section 1:   From the beginning to the end of page 45

  Question: *What did the earthquake do to the city?*

Section 2:   From the beginning of page 46 to the end

  Question: *What did the people do during the earthquake?*

- Encourage students to answer the test questions independently. If necessary, have them answer the questions orally in a group.
- For further support, have students work individually with you to answer the questions orally.

DISASTER!

In this theme you read about three very different kinds of disasters. Now you will read about a disaster that affected the lives of many Americans—the Great San Francisco Earthquake. You will also read an article about how people watch for earthquakes.

There are questions to answer before, during, and after your reading. You may go back to the selections to help you answer the questions.

1 READING STRATEGIES

1. **Self-Question**   Preview the first selection by reading the title and subtitles and looking at the pictures. Write one question you think will be answered as you read.

Score	0	1	2	3	4
Criterion	Illegible or no answer	Question not related to title and pictures	Question relates marginally to title and pictures; may repeat one of the selection's subheadings	Question relates generally to title and pictures	Question relates specifically to title and pictures
Sample Answer		*What is this test like.*	*Why do disasters like this always happen?*	*How many houses were not wrecked?*	*What did the people do when the earthquake struck?*

from ... If You Lived at the Time of the Great San Francisco Earthquake

by Ellen Levine
illustrated by Pat Grant Porter

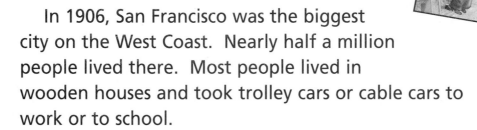

Introduction

In 1906, San Francisco was the biggest city on the West Coast. Nearly half a million people lived there. Most people lived in wooden houses and took trolley cars or cable cars to work or to school.

Very few people had automobiles, and nobody had radios or television sets — they weren't invented yet. Most people learned what was happening in the city and in other places by reading newspapers.

Then, on Wednesday, April 18, 1906, a terrible disaster struck San Francisco. A little after five o'clock in the morning, a huge earthquake hit the city.

The earth twisted, rumbled, and shook for nearly fifty seconds. If that seems like a short time to you, try jumping up and down for fifty seconds. You'll see that it feels much longer than it sounds.

Inside houses, pictures fell off the walls, lamps crashed to the floor, furniture raced around the room, books flew through the air, mirrors cracked into tiny pieces, walls caved in, and people were thrown from one end of a room to the other.

Three hours later, at eight o'clock in the morning, a second big quake hit the city. Then the earthquake was finally over. But the worst was still to come. For three days and nights, fires burned the city. The fires were so bright that you could read a newspaper at midnight. When it was over, there was little left of San Francisco. The city lay in ashes.

 Stop here and answer Question 2. Then continue reading.

READING STRATEGIES (continued)

2. **Predict/Infer**   What do you think the rest of the article will be about?

Score	0	1	2	3	4
Criterion	Illegible or no answer	Implausible prediction or unrelated response	Plausible prediction; not necessarily based on text or not elaborated	Plausible prediction based on text	Plausible and specific prediction based on text
Sample Answer		*That the earthquake will come three hours after each other.*	*Other earthquakes that happened*	*I think it talk more about the disaster*	*I think it will be about what it looked like after the earthquake and how people acted like.*

Rubric Score for Items 1–2 _____
8

What did San Francisco look like after the earthquake?

Everything was a mess! There were cracks in the streets that looked like giant zigzags. If you stood in one, it might be as high as your waist.

Telephone and electric wires had snapped and were hanging down from the poles. Cable car tracks that were in the ground were suddenly sticking up like huge, bent paper clips. And trolley car tracks lay twisted in the street.

Some trees had been pulled up by the roots. Branches were cracked and scattered around.

Chimneys had broken off rooftops throughout the city. Some chimneys had fallen inside homes, others were lying in the streets. In parts of the city, whole buildings had collapsed.

Walls of the new city hall building had fallen down. The dome was left standing on top of steel pillars. It had been the largest building in the state of California. After the earthquake, it looked like a skeleton.

The front wall of one hotel fell off completely, and the bedrooms looked like rooms in a doll's house. Can you imagine sitting in your bed and looking out at the street—with no windows in between!

Some buildings that were three or four stories high sank almost all the way into cracks in the ground. One nine-year-old girl remembered that her father took her out of their house through the attic window right onto the street.

Houses moved forward, backward, or sideways. If you went to bed on April 17th on one side of the street, you might have gotten up on April 18th across the street.

After the quake, one man climbed to the top of a hill and looked down on the city. From up high, people in the streets looked as if they were "running about like . . . excited insects."

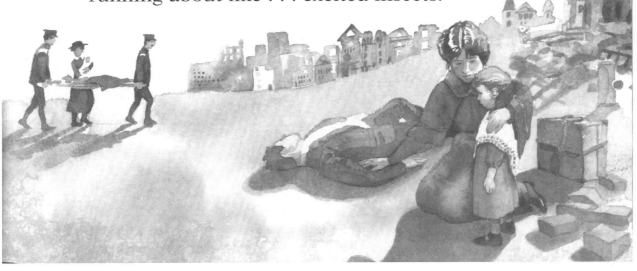

What did people do when the quake struck?

It was a little after five o'clock in the morning when the earthquake struck, and most people were asleep. It was a frightening way to wake up. Many people were so stunned that they ran straight out into the streets.

When they got outside, they realized that they were in their pajamas and nightgowns! Some didn't care and just stayed outside until the earth stopped shaking. Many people didn't take the time to put on shoes, and that was dangerous—there was broken glass all over the ground.

One man was seen running down the street with his pants on backward, his suspenders hanging down the front, and his shoes unlaced.

Another man was wearing his top hat and his fancy evening tailcoat. Underneath the coat, all he had on was his long underwear!

These people may have looked silly, but they were lucky to be alive and outside.

You just read about the Great San Francisco Earthquake. Now you will read about how scientists today learn about earthquakes.

Watching for Earthquakes

from Childcraft, Vol. 4, "People Who Study the World and Space"

Earthquakes happen all the time. We don't feel most of them. They are just small shakes in the earth. But some earthquakes make the ground tremble, rattle dishes, and even cause buildings to shake. And a few earthquakes smash and crumple buildings.

Seismologists are scientists who study earthquakes. Seismologists can't go underground to watch the rocks push, snap, and break. Instead, seismologists watch instruments called seismographs. These instruments help keep track of earthquakes all over the world—even the quakes we can't feel.

Seismographs are usually set on solid rock or inside vaults. There, they do not pick up vibrations caused by man-made things. But when an earthquake makes the earth shake, tremble, and shiver, it also moves a pen in the seismograph. The pen draws squiggly lines on a roll of paper.

Scientists use seismographs in groups of three. This way they can measure the east-west, north-south, and up-and-down ground motions of the earth.

A few times, seismologists have been able to predict earthquakes. But there is still much to learn about what causes earthquakes and when they will happen.

A scientist checks a seismographic reading for any unusual movement in the earth.

2 COMPREHENSION

Write your answers to these questions.

3. Why do you think the 1906 earthquake is called the Great San Francisco Earthquake? *(comprehension/critical thinking)*

Score	0	1	2	3	4
Criterion	Illegible or no answer	Inaccurate	Vague; may say it was very big	Tells generally that it caused great damage	Tells about the great damage it caused and gives examples
Sample Answer		*It was the first earthquake on earth.*	*It was very, very big!*	*because it did a lot of damage to the city*	*because it destroyed so many things and killed so many people*

4. Fill out the chart by writing the details that support the main idea. *(topic/main idea/supporting details)*

Topic: The Great San Francisco Earthquake

Main Idea: Much of San Francisco was destroyed as a result of an earthquake in April 1906.

Details:

Score	0	1	2	3	4
Criterion	Illegible or no answer	Inaccurate or irrelevant	Gives one detail that supports the main idea	Gives two details that support the main idea	Gives more than two details that support the main idea; may include descriptive words
Sample Answer		*The San Francisco Earthquake.*	*It moved houses all over.*	*Houses were crumbled, chimneys collapsed into houses.*	*Buildings and houses sank and rose. Mirrors and windows were scattered all around. Books flew off shelves. There were big cracks in the road. If you stood in a crack it would go up to your waist.*

5. What is the author's opinion of the Great San Francisco Earthquake? *(fact and opinion)*

Score	0	1	2	3	4
Criterion	Illegible or no answer	Inaccurate; may state a fact from selection	Gets close to opinion; talks about one aspect of the disaster	Gives opinion but does not give full extent of the disaster	States the author's opinion clearly
Sample Answer		*about a million people lived there*	*It caused San Francisco to be a wreck*	*It was a very very bad day.*	*The San Francisco Earthquake was a terrible disaster.*

6. Why are seismographs often set on solid rock or inside vaults? *(cause and effect)*

Score	0	1	2	3	4
Criterion	Illegible or no answer	Inaccurate; may restate question	Vague; may explain what seismographs do	Includes an accurate but incomplete thought	Gives a complete explanation of the reason
Sample Answer		*So it will not get wet.*	*So they can study earthquakes.*	*Because they pick up vibrations better.*	*They set seismographs on solid rock or inside vaults, because there they don't pick up vibrations from man-made things.*

Rubric Score for Items 3–6 _____
16

Read each question and fill in the circle next to the best answer. You may look back at the selections if you want to.

7. How do you think the people who lived far away in 1906 found out about the San Francisco earthquake? *(comprehension/critical thinking)*

    ○ a. They heard it on the radio.
    ● b. They read it in a newspaper.
    ○ c. They saw it on TV.
    ○ d. They read about it in a book.

8. In San Francisco, what caused more damage than the earthquakes? *(cause and effect)*

    ● a. fires that broke out all over the city
    ○ b. branches that were scattered around
    ○ c. broken glass all over the ground
    ○ d. cable car and train wrecks

9. Which detail about the Great San Francisco Earthquake is an opinion? *(fact and opinion)*

    ○ a. People ran out in their nightclothes.
    ● b. People looked like insects.
    ○ c. Streets cracked.
    ○ d. Trolley car tracks were twisted.

10. Why do scientists use three seismographs to record earthquakes? *(cause and effect)*

⬤ a. to record the different directions in which the ground moves

○ b. so that they can still record earthquakes even if one seismograph breaks

○ c. because the pen draws squiggly lines

○ d. so that they can be more certain of their recordings

11. Which sentence best describes how scientists learn about earthquakes? *(topic/main idea/supporting details)*

○ a. Scientists go underground to watch the rocks push, snap, and break.

○ b. Seismologists are scientists who study earthquakes.

⬤ c. Scientists use instruments called seismographs to measure ground motions of the earth.

○ d. Scientists use pens to draw squiggly lines on a roll of paper.

Score for Items 7–11 (x4) _____
20

3 WORD SKILLS

Read the sentence or sentences. Use what you know about figuring out new words to help you select the correct answer.

12. *In 1906, San Francisco was the <u>biggest</u> city on the West Coast.*

    How large was San Francisco? *(word endings -er and -est)*
    - ● a. It was larger than all the other cities in California.
    - ○ b. It was smaller than all the others in California.
    - ○ c. It was larger than most of the others in California.
    - ○ d. It was larger than some of the others in California.

13. *Chimneys had broken off rooftops <u>throughout</u> the city.*

    How would you divide the syllables in *throughout*? *(syllabication)*
    - ● a. through • out
    - ○ b. throu • ghout
    - ○ c. throug • hout
    - ○ d. througho • ut

14. *It was a frightening way to wake up. Many people were so <u>stunned</u> that they ran straight out into the streets.*

    How did the people feel? *(think about words)*
    - ○ a. hurt
    - ○ b. excited
    - ● c. shocked
    - ○ d. sleepy

15. *Earthquakes <u>happen</u> all the time.*

How would you divide the syllables in *happen*? *(syllabication)*
- ○ a. ha • ppen
- ● b. hap • pen
- ○ c. happ • en
- ○ d. h • appen

16. *And a few earthquakes smash and <u>crumple</u> buildings.*

What do a few earthquakes do to the buildings? *(think about words)*
- ● a. make them fall apart
- ○ b. leave them standing
- ○ c. move around them
- ○ d. move under them

17. *But when an earthquake makes the earth shake, tremble, and shiver, it also moves a pen in the seismograph.*

Which three words are synonyms? *(synonyms)*
- ○ a. earth, earthquake, seismograph
- ○ b. earthquake, makes, shake
- ○ c. earth, seismograph, move
- ● d. shake, tremble, shiver

Score for Items 12–17 (x4) _____
24

4 WRITING AND LANGUAGE

18. Write one or two paragraphs about one of the topics below.

    a. What if an earthquake happened where you live? How would you feel? What would it look like and feel like?

    b. Earthquakes, tornadoes, floods, and hurricanes are disasters that occur in nature. Write your own story about one of these disasters.

Scoring Rubric

Score	0	1	2	3	4
Criteria	illegible, no answer, or not related to prompt	•has no clear topic, or topic only vaguely relates to prompt •has little or no organization •has little or no use of details to explain reasoning behind answer •has limited or immature word choice •has major grammar, spelling, and mechanics errors	•states topic but may include unrelated ideas; may address both prompts •uses an organizational pattern with lapses •details to explain reasoning are not fully developed •has adequate word choice, not always precise •contains many grammar, spelling, and mechanics errors	•states topic clearly, and generally stays on subject •uses an organizational pattern with few lapses •uses adequate supporting details, but some may be irrelevant •has adequately precise word choice •contains a few grammar, spelling, and mechanics errors *or* •might have rated a 4 except for significant grammar, spelling, and mechanics errors	•focuses on topic throughout •uses a clear, consistent organizational pattern •uses many relevant supporting details to explain reasoning behind answer •usually precise and creative in word choice •contains few grammar, spelling, and mechanics errors

On the following pages you will find sample student responses for Question 18.

Rubric Score for Item 18 (x5) _____

20

Anchor Papers: *Sample Responses for Question 18 (Prompt a)*

Score 4: *The response addresses all aspects of the prompt. It is clearly organized to support the topic, and it gives a chronological description of events.*

If in an earthquake happened where I lived I would be frightened and scared. The buildings would be crumpled and only one building would stand afterwards and that would be the school. Everybody that is cold and hurt would go to the school.

If in an earthquake happened where I lived I would be frightened and scared. The buildings would be crumpled and only one building would stand afterwards and that would be the school. Every body that is cold and hurt would go to the school.

Score 3: *The answer addresses most of the aspects of the prompt but does not fully develop the details.*

If I were in an earthquake I would get to a safe spot. I would feel shocked and frightened. After it would look like a disaster.

If I were in an earthquake I would get to a safe spot. I would feel shocked and frightend. After it would look like a disaster.

Anchor Papers: *Sample Responses for Question 18 (Prompt a)*

Score 2: *The response addresses only parts of the prompt. The writing is basic and contains multiple spelling, grammar, and mechanics errors.*

If a earthquake happened to me I would be really scared I wouldn't know what to do and I wouldn't know what to think I would go wake up my mom and dad and tell them to see what they think the end.

> A If a earthquake happend to me I whould be reully scard I whoulden't no what to do and I whoulden't no what to think I whould go whake up my mum and dad and tell them to see what they think the end.

Score 1: *The response tries to address the prompts, but it does not give any supporting details. The word choice is simple.*

It would not be cool. I would feel sick.

> It would not be cool. I would feel sick.

Anchor Papers: *Sample Responses for Question 18 (Prompt b)*

Score 4: *The response demonstrates a clear understanding that this is a story. It follows a chronological order of events. It gives a concise description of the event.*

One day I was playing Nintendo. Then there was a earthquake. I turned the nintendo off. I have found a safe place. The earthquake went on for 60 seconds. Then it stopped. Then everything was ok. The end

One day I was playen Nintendo. Then, their was a earthquake. I turned the nintendo off. I have found a safe place. The earthquake went on for 6 0 seconds. Then it stoped. Then evey thing was ok. The end.

Score 3: *This is obviously a story. The writer gives the reader a vivid picture of what happened during the tornado. The word choice is especially effective. This story would have rated a 4 but for sentence fragments and punctuation mistakes.*

One day in a little town, a town that never really had any problems. But one day it was really really windy.

A tornado hit! It was terrible. Wooden houses got tore down. Glass windows broke into small pieces. It was so terrible

Then the tornado ended everyone was so happy, but it was still a mess. They cleaned everything.

One day in a little town, a town that never really had any problems. But one day it was really really windy.

A tornado hit! It was terrible. Wooden houses got tore down. Glass windows broke into small pieses; It was so terrible

Then the tornado ended everyone was so happy, but it was still a mess. They cleaned everything.

Anchor Papers: *Sample Responses for Question 18 (Prompt b)*

Score 2: *The writer realizes that this is a story, but the response has no stated topic and does not follow a logical order. This response contains many spelling, grammar, and mechanics errors.*

One day the world started. Some people did not know what was a happening. But it started to do it every. No one knew what was going on. But soon it was water every.

Everyone panicked and moved to the city and it never happen again. to then the water went down but they still did not move back again

> One day the world started. Some people didnot know what was happing. But it started to do it every. No one new what was going on But soon it was water every.
>
> everyone panket and I moved to the city. and it never happen a gone. to then the water went down but. they still Did not move back agen

Score 1: *The response does not answer the prompt. The writer does not tell what disaster is happening. There are many errors in grammar, spelling, and mechanics.*

I live in a wooden house the house is brown

I would not crying i will help people and me and my mom would run away

> I live in a wooden hous. the hous is brown
>
> I would not crying i will help people and me and my mom would run away

19. Read the letter below. Find and correct six errors. Use what you know about proofreading to make your corrections in the letter. The examples may help you. There are two spelling errors and four errors in verbs. *(vowel sound in* saw, *vowel + r sounds, verbs in the present, verbs in the past, the verb* be)

Dear Ted,

                                           has

Our trip~~p~~ to San Francisco ~~have~~ been a lot of fun.

                         ed

Last week we stayᴧ in a hotel near the bay. On the

first   **caught**   **ed**

~~furst~~ day, we went fishing. I ~~cawght~~ a little fish. I wantᴧ

to keep it, but my father made me throw it back.

    I bought you a present. But I won't tell you what it

             see   **are**

is until I ~~saw~~ you. I hope you ~~is~~ well.

                                        Love,

                                        Max

Base each student's score on the number of errors found and corrected, not on the student's use of proofreading marks. You may wish to refer students to the proofreading marks at the end of the Literacy Activity Book *Student Handbook.*

Score for Item 19 _____

                                            6

Combine each pair of sentences below by using compound predicates.

20. The ground was shaking. The ground was rumbling.

    (The ground was shaking and rumbling.)

    _____

    _____

    _____

    _____

21. The people were running. The people were helping each other.

    (The people were running and helping each other.)

    _____

    _____

    _____

    _____

Score for Items 20–21 (x3) _____

6

Write a letter to a friend or family member. Your letter should show that you have thought about what you have read.

Dear _____,

From reading the theme Disaster! I learned _____

_____

_____.

Some new words I learned in this theme were _____

_____

_____.

The best part of Disaster! was _____

_____

_____.

I really liked this part because _____

_____

_____

_____.

Sincerely,

_____

ALTERNATIVE FORMAT INTEGRATED THEME TESTS

LEVEL 3.1

Enjoy

USING THE ALTERNATIVE FORMAT TESTS

USING AND ADMINISTERING

Purpose

The Alternative Format Tests provide an opportunity for all students to participate in the evaluation process. By providing summaries of the theme-related text selections and comprehension questions that may be answered orally, each Alternative Format Test enables you to evaluate more accurately the progress of students who may otherwise have difficulty accessing the text selections.

Description

The Alternative Format Tests include summaries of the authentic reading selections used in the Integrated Theme Tests. Students are asked to respond to the selections by answering comprehension questions. The comprehension questions are in written-response and multiple-choice formats. However, depending on ability level, students may give their answers orally.

Administering the Alternative Format Tests

Administer the Alternative Format Tests at the same time and in the same manner as you would administer the Integrated

Theme Tests. Students taking the Alternative Format Tests should feel that they are participating in the same process as their classmates.

- **Grouping:** The Alternative Format Tests can be administered individually or in a small group. However, if you have several students who may be answering the comprehension questions orally, you may find it easier to evaluate each student if you administer the tests individually.

- **Pacing:** Most students will be able to complete the test in 30–40 minutes. Allow enough time for students to finish the test without rushing.

Guidelines for Scoring

Answers are provided in the answer key on page T23. Score 1 point for each item answered correctly. If a student scores a 4 or 5 on an Alternative Format Test, continue with extra support and consider using the standard Integrated Theme Test when evaluating the student at the end of the next theme. If a student consistently scores 3 or below on the Alternative Format Tests, you may want to reconsider your instructional approach or the level of difficulty of the materials the student is using.

Name _____

**Read the summary of the story "Papa Pig and His Three Sons."
Then answer the questions that follow. You can look back at the
summary for help.**

Papa Pig and His Three Sons

Papa Pig had three sons. They lived with him in a big brick house. One day, Papa told his sons it was time to build their own houses. Papa told them about the big bad wolf. He told them to build strong brick houses. Then the wolf could not get in.

The next day, the little pigs left home. The first pig built a straw house. The second pig built a wood house. It did not take long. They were ready to play.

They ran to see the third little pig. He was building a brick house. He wanted to be safe from the wolf. The first two pigs made fun of their brother. "We're already done," they said. Then they went fishing.

As the two pigs fished, the wolf came along. He chased the pigs. They ran to the straw house. They shut the door. But the wolf huffed and puffed. He blew the house down! So the pigs ran to the wood house. But the wolf blew down that house too!

This time, the pigs ran to Papa Pig's house. They were safe. The wolf could not blow down a brick house. He did not even try.

Alternative Format Tests, Level 3.1   Oink, Oink, Oink   **T17**

The next day, the two little pigs went to see their brother. They helped him build a strong, safe brick house. And they all lived in it happily ever after.

1. Why didn't the first and second pigs use bricks?

_____

_____

2. Why did the third pig build a house out of bricks?

_____

_____

3. How many houses did the wolf blow down?
   - ○ a. one
   - ○ b. two
   - ○ c. three
   - ○ d. none

4. Why didn't the wolf try to blow down Papa Pig's house?
   - ○ a. He knew he could not do it.
   - ○ b. He was tired.
   - ○ c. He was the pigs' friend.
   - ○ d. His mother told him to come home.

5. What did the first two pigs learn?
   - ○ a. Two plus two equals four.
   - ○ b. how to bake a cake
   - ○ c. how to catch a fish
   - ○ d. A brick house is best.

Name _____

Read the summary of the story *We Keep a Store*. Then answer the questions that follow. You can look back at the summary for help.

We Keep a Store

by Anne Shelby

A little girl and her family keep a store. It is in their front yard. The whole family works in the store. The girl likes working together with her family.

The store has a big box of candy. When someone wants candy, the girl's mother scoops it out of the box. Then she puts it in a sack and weighs it. Sometimes the little girl eats a piece of candy from the box. But only when her mother isn't looking.

The girl's mother orders things for the store. She orders them from a big company. When the boxes come, the girl's father opens them. The girl helps stack cans on shelves.

Sometimes people come to the store just to visit. Men sit together and tell stories. Women sit under the tree and clean green beans or cut up apples. Children play games they make up.

At dark, it is time for everyone to go home. The girl's father tells the people to come back. They say they will. The girl says that's the very best thing about keeping a store.

1. What does "keep a store" mean?

    _____

    _____

    _____

2. What is the best thing about keeping a store for the girl?

    _____

    _____

    _____

3. Where is the family's store?
    ○   a. on the main street
    ○   b. in a mall
    ○   c. in their front yard
    ○   d. in a park

4. What does the girl help with?

    ○   a. packing boxes
    ○   b. telling stories
    ○   c. cutting apples
    ○   d. stacking cans

5. Why do people come to the store?

    ○   a. to buy things and to visit
    ○   b. to sew a new dress
    ○   c. to fix their cars
    ○   d. to check out books

Name _____

Read the summary of the selection *If You Lived at the Time of the Great San Francisco Earthquake*. Then answer the questions that follow. You can look back at the summary for help.

from . . . If You Lived at the Time of the Great San Francisco Earthquake

by Ellen Levine
illustrated by Pat Grant Porter

In 1906, San Francisco was the biggest city on the West Coast. Nearly 500,000 people lived there. Most people lived in wooden houses. Few people had cars. TVs and radios had not been made yet.

On April 18, disaster hit! A huge earthquake started just after five in the morning. The earth twisted and shook for almost one minute. Three hours later, a second big quake hit. Finally, the earth was still.

San Francisco was a mess! Streets had huge cracks in them. Wires hung down from poles. Trees had been pulled up by the roots. Whole buildings had fallen down. Houses had moved all around. Some sank into the ground. One girl and her father climbed out their attic window. They went right onto the street!

Right after the quake, many people ran out into the streets. Most of them had been sleeping. Some were still in their nightclothes!

But the worst had not happened yet. The earthquake started fires. The fires spread through the city. San Francisco burned for three days. Not much was left when the fires died. The city was ruined.

1. How did the city look after the earthquake?

     _____

     _____

2. What happened for three days after the earthquake?

     _____

3. When did the great earthquake hit San Francisco?
     ○   a. December 11, 1995
     ○   b. July 4, 1776
     ○   c. April 18, 1906
     ○   d. February 3, 1971

4. How long did the first big quake last?

     ○   a. almost one minute
     ○   b. almost one hour
     ○   c. almost one day
     ○   d. almost thirty minutes

5. Why did people run out into the streets in their nightclothes?

     ○   a. The earthquake had not hit yet.
     ○   b. They wanted to show off their new clothes.
     ○   c. The earthquake hit while they were sleeping.
     ○   d. It was three hours later.

ANSWER KEY TO ALTERNATIVE FORMAT TESTS

The answers to the written-response questions are sample answers.
Accept any answers that contain the information provided.

Theme 1: Oink, Oink, Oink
1. They wanted to play.
2. He wanted to be safe from the wolf.
3. b. two
4. a. He knew he could not do it.
5. d. A brick house is best.

Theme 2: Community Ties
1. The family owns (or works in) a store.
2. visiting with the people who come there
3. c. in their front yard
4. d. stacking cans
5. a. to buy things and to visit

Theme 3: Disaster!
1. Everything was a mess. Buildings had fallen down. Houses were moved around. Trees were uprooted. Wires were hanging. Streets were cracked.
2. Fires burned the city.
3. c. April 18, 1906
4. a. almost one minute
5. c. The earthquake hit while they were sleeping.

ACKNOWLEDGMENTS

"Watching for Earthquakes," from *World and Space*, vol. 4 of *Childcraft: The How and Why Library*. Copyright © 1985 by World Book, Inc. Reprinted by permission.

We Keep a Store, by Anne Shelby. Text copyright © 1990 by Anne Shelby. Reprinted by permission of Orchard Books, New York.

"Wolf," from *The World Book Encyclopedia*, Volume 21. Copyright © 1995 by World Book, Inc. Reprinted by permission.

CREDITS

Illustrations 4, 6–8, T17 Kristen Goeters; **22–26, T19** Colin Bootman

Photographs 27 Rory Freed; **47** Russell D. Curtis/Photo Researchers, Inc.

INVITATIONS
TO LITERACY

ISBN 0-395-74988-3

9 780395 749883

90000>

Houghton Mifflin

Boston Atlanta Dallas Geneva, Illinois Palo Alto Princeton

1-35136-**3.1**